This edition published in 2011 by Waverley Books,
144 Port Dundas Road, Glasgow, G4 0HZ, Scotland

© 2011 Waverley Books

ISBN 978 1 84934 054 0

Printed and bound in China

HOW DO SKELETONS CALL THEIR FRIENDS? ON THE TELEBONE!

WHAT DO YOU CALL A SKELETON WHO WON'T GET UP IN THE MORNINGS? LAZY BONES!

WHAT'S A SKELETON'S FAVOURITE MUSICAL INSTRUMENT? A trom-bone!

What is a skeleton's favourite drink? Milk – it's so good for the bones!

WHY DID THE SKELETON STAY OUT IN THE SNOW ALL NIGHT LONG?

He was a numbskull.

WHAT DO YOU CALL A STUPID SKELETON?

Bonehead!

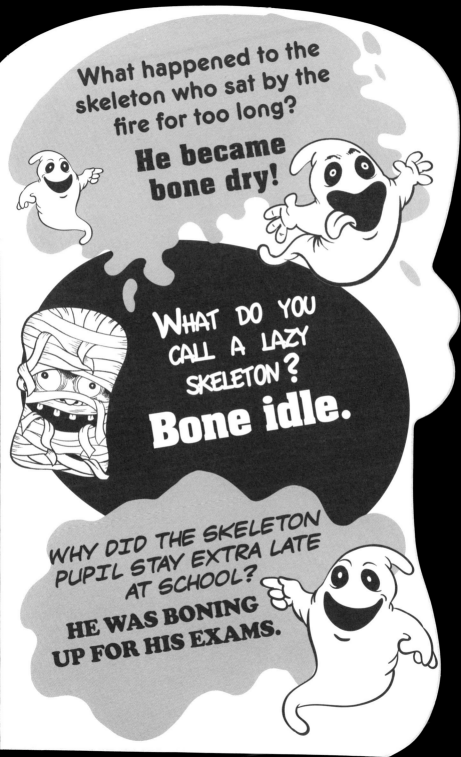

WHAT DO YOU CALL A SKELETON DOCTOR?

BONES.

WHAT SORT OF SOUP DO SKELETONS LIKE?

SOUP WITH PLENTY OF BODY IN IT!

WHAT HAPPENED TO THE SKELETON WHO WAS SWALLOWED BY A HUGE FISH?

HE HAD A WHALE OF A TIME!

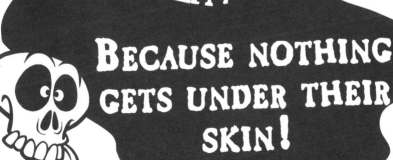

WHAT HAPPENED TO THE SKELETON THAT WAS ATTACKED BY A DOG?

THE DOG RAN OFF WITH SOME BONES AND DIDN'T LEAVE HIM WITH A LEG TO STAND ON.

WHY ARE SKELETONS SO CALM?

BECAUSE NOTHING GETS UNDER THEIR SKIN!

WHY DIDN'T THE SKELETON WANT TO PLAY FOOTBALL?

Because his heart wasn't in it!

WHAT HAPPENED TO THE SKELETON WHO WENT TO A PARTY?

Everyone used him as a coat rack!

WHAT DID THE GHOULS' FAVOURITE HOTEL HAVE AS A FEATURE?

IT HAD RUNNING ROT AND MOULD!

WHAT DOES THE POSTMAN BRING TO VAMPIRES?

FANG MAIL!

What does a vampire stand on after having a bath?

A BAT MAT !

Why did the vampire attack the clown?

He wanted the circus to be in his blood.

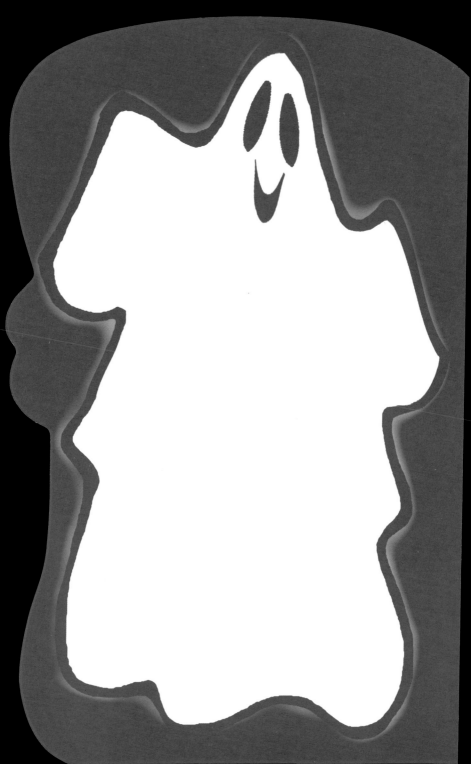

What is a vampire's favourite soup? **Scream of mushroom !**

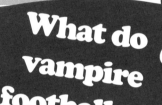

What do vampire footballers have at half-time?

Blood oranges !

WHEN DO VAMPIRES BITE YOU?

CHEWSDAY AND WINCEDAY.

What happened when the cannibals had a wedding?

They toasted the bride and groom!

What's the best way to help a starving cannibal?
Give him a hand!

What do cannibals eat with cheese on toast?
Pickled organs!

MONSTER (WITH VERY BIG FEET): I WOULD LIKE TO SEE SOME BOOTS THAT WILL FIT ME.

SALES ASSISTANT: SO WOULD I, SIR.

DID YOU HEAR ABOUT THE HANDSOME BOY MONSTER MEETING THE BEAUTIFUL GIRL MONSTER?

IT WAS LOVE AT FIRST FRIGHT!

HOW WAS THE WITCH AFTER SHE WAS RUN OVER BY A TRUCK?

TYRED!